Letters From Your Neighbour Far Away

For all who enjoy writing

Crumps Barn Studio
Crumps Barn, Syde, Cheltenham GL53 9PN
www.crumpsbarnstudio.co.uk

Cover design and illustrations by Lorna Gray

Printed in Gloucestershire on FSC certified paper by Severn, a
carbon neutral company

ISBN 978-1-915067-08-1

Letters From Your Neighbour Far Away

BEVERLEY GORDON

Collected Poems

Crumps Barn Studio

My dear neighbours

At a distance, I bring you peace, I bring you joy.

How are you all? I sit here today looking out to the distance watching the birds come and go

And at times I wonder how far they fly? Where do they go? What do they see?

So I thought why not write to you all near and far

So I call in my birds and train them to carry my letter to you each day all it took was some time – many years to perfect their training

But now they are ready to go

As I do not know you all or have no address, my birds will find the right door

They will drop off each letter by a window or a door in the garden or on a tree or a balcony

That you can reach. All I ask of you in return please

Leave a sip of water so that they can quench their beak for the journey back. If you have a letter of reply please put it in the same spot, tie a little ribbon around it – it'll be much easier for them to carry back

Where I am I cannot buy stamps or find a post box

But I'd like to hear from as many of you if I can

Your highs your lows a story from long ago

People don't write anymore. It's a phone or text even email oh how the world has grown

There are many neighbours out there who would like a little note

A little hello, I care to know. You are all connected from long ago. But the world has gotten so big

Many have lost, some have forgotten.

But I am here wanting to say hello to you all, how is your day and week going

Your name you don't have to give – just my neighbour will do

Let's have some fun and let the writing begin.

Your neighbour
From a distant land

Hello neighbour

I found your letter in my tree house

It's not very big, Daddy built it for me

I saw your bird, it was a big one looking at me – I was scared I thought it would peck me

But the nasty boy next door threw a stone at it

But it flew away. But not before it pooped on his head he ran in his house

It was so funny.

How many birds do you have?

I have a cat called Tiny and a dog called Sneeze, he's always sneezing

I wanted a bird but Daddy says it's not nice to have them locked up in a cage

Do your birds have names? I have a good name for your bird – you can name him Claw

On account of his big feet.

I don't go out much, I sit by my window most of the days I have a tutor

She is very nice, a nurse comes to see me once a week

I get very tired but your letter makes me smile

What other animals do you have?

I am learning to paint. I am going to paint your bird, will he come again?

I must go now. I have to take my medicines, it's not nice

I try to hide it under my tongue. But clever Daddy knows hahaha

Bye now

Dear neighbour

What a good idea. People don't talk any more so much violence and crime

Me, I am here doing time – drugs get the better of me so I hurt and steal to satisfy my needs

You see I hang around with bad companies, my parents warn me

Go to school get a degree leave those bad companies that you call your extended families

So here I am spending time because I refuse to listen I thought what do they know I did not see them having fun when I was growing up alone for they were too busy for me

Plus they smoke and drink, so who are they to discipline me

Do I have regrets well yes look where it has gotten me

They have not come to see me. Too ashamed I guess

They always have to keep up this appearance. What would the neighbours think

They told them I have gone to boarding school.

Too ashamed to face the fact that I am locked up in a prison cell

Do I have regrets I guess so, do I blame them, used to

But now I have plenty of time to reflect. I will write
to them

And see. I have taken up a few classes whilst I am in here
hahaha just thinking it's like boarding school we get to go
out in the courtyard for exercise each day

The food is not so bad. Could do with a touch more salt

I like what you say "All things are lawful, but not all
things build up. Let each one keep

Seeking, not his own advantage, but that of the other
person" (1 Corinthians 10:23,24)

You went on to say "just because we have the freedom
to do something does not mean that we should do it.
We must think carefully about how our decisions affect
others."

You are so right, are you a religious person?

I never have the time for God I was too busy having fun
well you are only young once

But in here there is plenty of time to try something new
I guess

I'll let you know if they write back or visit

Neighbour through a bar window

Hello neighbour

Got one of your letters today. It so happened to be on the bird house

No I don't keep birds but now and then they would come to feed

I have some bad news and good news. But first let me tell you about my neighbour, his garden backs on to mine. We call him Mr Fix-it.

Mr Fix-it is a very very nice man slightly tone deaf but there is nothing that he cannot fix

We all love him never a dull moment when he is around he also loves to sing

Like I said he is tone deaf he likes to try his hand at other things

So this particular day Mr Fix-it got it into his head he wanted to learn how to play golf yes golf. So he bought a set of golf clubs and decided while we were all still in bed he was going to have a practice in his back garden – 6 am. Well you can just imagine the horror

Every neighbour got woken up, we thought it was the end of the world

There were balls going everywhere from rooftop to conservatory

Mr Fix-it was at it again. This time no one was happy, everyone knocked on his door holding golf balls.

When Mr Fix-it came to the door he did not look fazed at all, it was so surreal he smiled and took the balls and said thank you so kind of you I was running out of balls and closed the door leaving everyone with a look of disbelief so they knocked on the door but no answer, you see he has a special bell that when you ring it, there is a light bulb that flashes at the back of the garden when he is there to let him know that someone is at the door

So they kept knocking and calling no Mr Fix-it he was too bus practicing his golf swing

Eventually someone touched the bell – yes me – Mr Fix-it came to the door

All were talking at once finally everyone calmed down while one person spoke up

Yes, me again speaking for all. After explaining to him the damage he had caused

"Oh dear oh dear that will never do," he said, "I will get my tools."

Well he spent the whole weekend fixing the damage

The bad news, your bird got hurt by one of his golf balls

We took it to the vet he will be OK well enough to fly but not yet

His wing will take a little while to heal, I am so sorry

Mr Fix-it was very sad he sat with the bird at night the vet could not refuse

He took back the golf kit to the store

We all felt sorry for him so we treated him to some golf lessons on a proper golf course

Once the bird makes a good recovery we'll keep
you posted

Kind regards,

Your neighbours distant shore

Greetings my neighbour

From the land where sunshine and the cool warm breeze never ends

Where tropical birds come out to play and the doctor birds

That you might know as hummingbirds go about their busy day

Inspecting the plants as they lance their flowers

Yes neighbour, this is going to be a very busy day

As I get ready to pick the first ripe fruits from my tree

To be shipped to market, hope I will make a profit

The children are up early, work on the farm needs to be done

Their school is not far away. In fact, where we are, their school you can see from a distance

It's situated on what was once a little farm

The old man who once owned it left it in his will for a school to be built

He used to collect all our children, took them on his tractor to a school

Some distance away. And at weekends all the children would help him

On his little farm. But since he has passed away, the little farm which will soon be gone

Has helped the children in so many ways.

As a single mum you know I have so little time. So much work on my mind

Cannot find the time to write all I want to say

You have a good day, thanks for stopping by

From your neighbour a long distance away

Good evening to you neighbour

My evening brings out the stars, they sparkle against the dark heaven

I try to count them but they are too many so I pull up a deckchair

And just lose myself within the atmosphere

I went for a stroll earlier among the tall grass a place where crickets like to play

I caught some fireflies in a jar very handy when you have no candle for the night

But I will release them once I go to bed.

I took a deep breath, it was a calm night no cloud in sight

The neighbour across the way have also come out to refresh herself in the

Night cool air after a hard day of baking bread those sweet smells fill the air

Such a delicious smell, I must remember to put my order in

I can see my other neighbour chasing her children around the house trying to

Get them into their beds

Oh the neighbour on the hill is having a BBQ

this is the only time we are able to get together to

exchange chats on how our day has been

Mrs B has fallen asleep I have to go wheel her to bed

She likes her little cider that goes straight to her head

One night she almost fell in the well

Another time she fell out of bed. Mrs B is really something else

But one of the nicest people you could ever meet

But now we have to lower her be … oh!

Sorry they are calling me, I have to go

Good night my neighbour thanks for checking up on me

How are you doing neighbour

It has been one of those days no school this week
Little man scrapes his knees climbing a tree
Little miss catches chickenpox
Little big man is nowhere to be seen
Oh my what a day I am having
Walk with me if you please here I am under this very
tall tree
The branches are long and strong – little man likes to
Climb high and swing off them so I am tying a
rope around
The tree to make it easy for his little knees
As he loves to climb this tree Oh yes that's much better
Next I go among the plant a special leaf I will pick
To help little miss with her chickenpox I will blend it to
smooth her hitch
Little big man rises early with the morning sun –
off he runs
I hope he won't be too long, it's going to be a very busy
week for me

I must go now little ones will need their tea
A father's work is never done.

Nice to hear from you neighbour

Hello my neighbour

It's a cloudy day looking over the horizon

It's going to rain I feel a chill in the air

Where I am from, it seems to rain every day

With the lightning and thunder I must stay indoors

The rain will not go away it's just another depressing day

But for the plants and trees they are in a land of luxury

Even the animals' pond will be filled, they'll be having a good drink

My washing I cannot hang on the line

A wooden fire I must make if these clothes are going to dry this week

The electric is not switched on for fear the lightning will strike the rooftop

I cannot go to the shop until the rain has stopped

So you see I am not having a good day.

From your neighbour far away

Dear neighbour

The land where I am from the war is still going on
Many lives have been lost, many tears have begun
Bodies lying on the streets young and old
A mother's tears cannot be controlled
A father's desperate search for his wife and child
That he still cannot find, he cannot be
Consoled
The smell of the bad air cannot go away
I am in despair for I so long for peace
What the war is about I really don't know
For we cannot take anything with us
Where someday we might go
I close my eyes and set my mind free into a world
Where war is no more
But for now I hug my pillow at night and cry
myself to sleep
Hoping this is just a bad dream
So neighbour. Pray for all of us if you please
For I do not know if this will be my last communication
to you

For tomorrow is another day I do not know what will come my way.

Your neighbour a distance away

Dear neighbour

Oh what can I say where should I start

It has been a struggle this past year

Lost my job that I had for 40 years

Never have I been one day late, but times of changes

I got a letter of redundancy would you believe it in
the post

What is this I plead, is that how the company treats me

After 40 years of loyalty

I was so angry and dismayed I had no clue they gave
nothing away

I would have been happy to work 3 days or take less
of a pay

That's how much I wanted to stay but no offer was
put my way

You see I am old and a little grey. oh! All right a lot
of grey

But still I can pull my weight

My neighbour I have no family did not have the time

I work and play. A family it's something I put off
each time

Did I save no not really as I say I work and play

When I am not working I am on
expensive holiday

My pension is yet another 4 years away

So you see nothing is going my way.

Your neighbour old and grey

Dear neighbour

Thank you for your kind words

I spoke to them as you say

It's not that they did not want me

As they explain.

They apologise and ask me to stay

The experience I have they could not throw it away, they create a position for me within the company

Just 3 days a week for the same pay but now I am training those who are joining the company sometime in May

It's only until I come to my pension age which will be in 4 years

I will be a little wiser and save. No more expensive holidays

OK maybe just one a year

Remember I say I have no family, well I got a puppy today

I will name her after you, by the way.

What's your name?

Your neighbour

Dear neighbour

I jump up with a big bang over my head
That made me fall out of bed.
Those neighbours of mine do not consider the time
What are they banging I ask myself
Oh my poor head I had some drinks with my friends
I think I overdid it coffee where are you when I
need one
Holy moley this is not my bed
Would you believe it I did not go home
I do not know whose bed I found myself in
So I quickly got out the door then I could not find my
car key
Still not fully focused I walked down some long hallway
I could hear shouting and banging.
Oh coffee where are you when I need one
It must have been some strange drink I cannot really
recall a thing
Thank you, someone just handed me a cup of something
to drink
Yak! They call this coffee. Tastes like cats hmm!
Excuse me please

So as my senses return you are not going to believe where
I was – try and guess

I was in a jail cell, not locked in

A policeman saw the state I was in and took my keys for
my safety

And let me spend the night in a cell. No I was
not charged

I was very embarrassed. Why you may ask

I was dressed in a rabbit suit so they all had a good laugh

So no, I did not smile today. Has anyone got an aspirin?
oh! My head

Catch you later neighbour

Hello neighbour

Even though we may be strangers far away I feel I can talk to you

You see I work in a factory that sells expensive mannequins that look real

Their body feels like human flesh

Yes that's right, mannequins. So my friends and I decided to have a bet

After a couple of drinking shots went to our head

You know have some fun, when the factory was closed we would slip in through the back door

Take some photos have a laugh

So we would strip off down to our bare essentials and pose along side

Other mannequins – these mannequins are not to be handled so they are placed on a conveyor belt

And as it goes along it would be wrapped no not head to toe but just halfway

A simple throw over to cover their delicate parts

So there I was lying still daring not to breathe, I felt a large wind rolling around my system.

Only thing was the caretaker of the mannequins was in and he was short-sighted I did not think he was in today so when we saw him we

Decided to jump off the conveyor belt before he could come near us

Well you can imagine what happened next, I did not get off in time the conveyor belt started to move

I was there signalling to my friends when I heard a click I looked down both my ankles were handcuffed my eyes almost popped out of my head the others managed to get off before I could and run to get dressed

I could not say or do a thing I did not want to get fired you see we were having a drink

As I got close to him he was just about to stamp my behind

When a voice called out to him, no it was not my friends

It was the manager I thought everyone was gone

Caretaker he calls him bring me one of those mannequin

Which one that one as he pointed to me. Poor me still doing my best to keep still

Not wanting to breath and keep this wind in that is not good for my system as he put me on to the trolley and pushed me toward the office

I glanced at my friends who had come back but hiding behind the box

And looking horrified at the same time trying to control their laughter

My eyes signalling to them to do something.

As I was being pushed towards the lift to go up one floor, I wanted to wee

My friends took the stairs got to the floor just in time for the lift door to open

Then they tried to distract the caretaker with complimentary chat

While the next one tried to uncuff my leg. That wind I could not contain it just had to come out of my system that very moment. They all turned and look at the caretaker who did not pay them any mind

But the manager came out of his office and thought that the girls were

Helping him. Thank you girls we can take it from here you go home now

Bring it in here he said as I was pushed into the room trying hard to hold my pee

The room was full of buyers. My heart was beating out my chest

So what happened next you want to know. So do I for I passed out

All right I did not pass out. But it gets worse as the buyers gathered around to examine the merchandise, yes me the one pretending to be a mannequin. I could hear one man say this is remarkable. It feels so real touching my chest.

Where does the battery go? My eyeballs nearly pop out my head

I felt like I was in the twilight zone my so-called friend could not contain their laughter

As they watched behind the glass door

While the manager sent the caretaker for a battery.

What happen next wouldn't you want to know, I felt one of the buyers dribble as he sniffed my neck. It did not end. One of them squeezed my butt, saying remarkable, remarkable

Panic took over me I could feel my pee wanting to be released I did not know what to do

They continued their chatting, as their attention turned away from me for a moment I signalled to my friends to do something. Did I realise that pervert of a buyer was still watching me,

I thought to myself he must know he must know, he came over again staring in my face

A little dribble running down his lips I held my breath, just then the caretaker came in, with the largest battery you can imagine

Yes it happened, I peed and peed, the room was silent looking at me the Manager's eyes and mouth open wide. The pervert buyer gasped and stepped aside

Ankle still cuffed I turn and say excuse me please and hop out the room

Then I woke up, it was only a bad dream.

When I went to work the next day I was getting funny looks with a smile

I was so puzzled I call my friend over and ask why are they smiling

Don't you know she says then the manager calls me to his office

You are not going to believe it. He wants to use my size and shape to make a mannequin model

Yes neighbour I do work in a factory and yes I dress the mannequins there

We sell mannequins of different sizes and shapes

He has some buyers coming in so he wants to show me off to them.

Yep you guessed it

I found a new job.
In a supermarket.

Take care neighbour until I write again

Dear neighbour

Where I am from we have plenty of snow

You must come here one day there is so much fun
to be had

I will treat you to a hot chocolate with marshmallows

Relaxing near a wood burning fire

I have a little cabin near by the lake

Do you like fishing, but we will have to break the ice
to catch some fish

I don't have a fishing rod, so I tie a hook on a string
with some bait and sit and wait

It's a long wait. This is where I am now dropping you
a line. Get it dropping you a line hahaha

Yesterday I caught two fish a little small so I put
them back

I had to open a can of spam for supper. I will try
again tomorrow

Did you know when you look close up at a snowflake
no two flakes are the same

Snow is not really that cold or maybe it's because I am
overdressed with lots of layers

Either way we have plenty of snow.

When you look at the cabin from a distance it's a picture postcard

Situated between some fern trees, the fern tree is covered with dripping snow

Then the smoke from the cabin chimney really sets it off

I will take a picture and post it to you.

Thanks for asking about my weekend away

Have a nice day neighbour

Dear neighbour

I am not having a good day

It's sad to say I got burgled today

They have taken the things that mean so much to me

My puppy that I call Alfree, it's a pedigree really expensive indeed

It used to curl up next to me oh how I did not hear or see

You see I had a long day very tired I was

So I came home and went straight to bed

Nothing else was taken that I could see

There was no mess no disturbances

I check the camera I could only see that they removed their shoes

Not wanting to disturb me, how polite of them I have to comment

I check the outside camera what is this I see

I've only gone and left the key in the door

Was I that tired when I open the door, it's not like me

Now my puppy is no more. Then I heard a tap on the back door

A little crying was getting louder as I came closer to the back door

I open it to find it's Alfree my puppy was by the door
with a note
Attached to his collar it read:

Don't leave you key in the door – you are lucky I am
turning a new leaf
Burglary is what I don't do any more

My neighbour. I can only thank God for this day
And the ex-burglar for not taking Alfree my puppy away.

You have a nice day
Your neighbour somewhere

Dear neighbour

Good day I want to ask you a question if you please –
how can you tell if you are in love?

How many types of love are there?

You see I met this boy a long time ago well, when I say
met him I mean from a distance

That first look when our eyes met I was hooked. I get
very shy when he looks at me. My stomach turns over my
heart wants to skip a beat .I have only said hello to him a
few times but never a deep conversation

But the ladies are crazy over him so I am told, so I just
keep at a distance

He does not keep bad company nor is he flirtatious not
that I can see

I have dated many guys but none have captivated me as
he does – don't get me wrong they all are very nice in
their own right but they were just not the ones for me

I'd like to get to know him better without tripping over
my tongue or having anxiety

He has that smile that lights up a thousand stars and eyes
that you can get lost within

My heart beats like I have a large orchestra playing in my
chest whenever our eyes link

His ears stick out, it shows up more when he has a
hair cut

But that's minor

I remember you once made a quote. It says you have to
like before you can love what did you mean by that? And

What do you think I should do I am going off campus for
a week or two

Hear from you soon Neighbour

Hello!

Miss goody two shoes miss nicey-nicey

Trying to get everyone writing talking

Look, around the world has gone to pot

It's everyman for themselves I have no time for people,
people have no time for me

You show love it gets trampled on. Long gone the days
of kindnesses, hello ignorance

Are you living in space? Can you not see and hear
people crying, children hungry

The rich getting rich, while the poor have no home to
call their own

The rich take their home and land then build tower
blocks and charge them rent

Like I say it's a world of miserable me First people

What are you getting out of this, those poor birds
working so hard for what –

Why don't you not grow two pairs of wings and
fly yourself

By the way your bird poops in my garden, lucky my cat
was not about

So what if I am miserable, what has the world done
for me

I lost my job about to lose my home, I have no car
could not afford the petrol

Here the government don't help so everyone's on the
hustle, crime rate sky high every day someone gets
killed so stop trying to do the impossible people

Don't want to know unless your letters come with
a cheque

I have no time for your nonsense

Good day.

Dear ones

Life is not like we once knew it. It was hard then, it's even harder now

New challenges each one faces every day no matter your age or lifestyle

But what keeps the world spinning is the love from heaven above as we wake up and look, and give thanks for your eyes to see another day

Unforeseen circumstances befall us all some harder than others

A person of little wants what the person of plenty has

The person of plenty wants what the person of little has, for what the person of plenty has can weigh them down

Yet neither appreciate the value of what is important yet they both have it, no not material possession. Life itself

Today many are angry at life, at the world.

At each other, but never stop for a moment to hear their heartbeat

Yes the seeing of the world is changing, do you not agree, do you change with it?

Do you ride it like a surfer riding the wave hoping not to fall off?

One look at the world through clouded lenses

Instead of stopping for a moment to wipe them clear

How many of you have stopped on a clear night and looked to the sky and counted the stars?

Life is what you make it, so it has been said. If a person stands still and watches, time runs off with their dream because they could not be bothered to get out of bed. Is it right or fear to envy another person's success?

There is an old saying in a very old book of proverbs 6v 6-11 – it's speak of the Ants

You see, you would like me to quote it here.

But how about you getting off your lazy chair

And go and have a look for that old book somewhere gathering dust.

Let's not beat down those who try to bring a smile to others, who are so much in need – the world is full of colour, you just have to clean those lenses to see it to appreciate it.

Love thy neighbours

Dear neighbour

I had some sad news last week

I got a letter from my uncle saying my brother has passed away

He took his life. Right now I feel so empty inside

I cannot stop thinking it's my fault. We haven't spoken for a while

Over something silly, so I moved away

He started to drink heavily. I had a prestigious job

I had no time for him. He would call me but I would always make an excuse

Too busy with work. At that time I really did not care

My uncle tried to get me to help him, I refused. My brother wrote to me a number of times

I did not even open the letters, I just threw them aside. Now I open his letters tears roll down my eyes

It was saying how sorry he was and how much he loved me

It went on to say he had a family

She died giving birth

The child a sweet little girl looks like me also passed away

He cannot find any comfort so he drinks to take the pain away

His last letter says forgive me my dear sister

You would have made a beautiful aunt but I must join them today.

My dear neighbour I cannot control the pain I could have helped him instead I turned

My back on him

Over some silly arguments that I cannot even remember

What it was about

He is my only Brother

When I reflect back what do I really have – no family

Not even a child to call my own. The job I had which I thought

Would give me all I need. Sorry neighbour I have to stop there

If you please.

Hope one day we can meet
Your neighbour

Dear neighbour

I have a new job in a nursery, looking forward to it –
I never worked with young ones

Age 6 months and over, I never knew you can put
them in nursery so young

My goodness this should be fun

I worked with older ones in school nursery,

So this would be my first encounter with babies of
little age,

The day did not go so well

I got puked on, scream in my ears, when it became
time to change the

nappies, I wish their bottom comes with a warning
sign. I need a big nose peg

Then I spend the rest of the day chasing little Johnny
man! He is quick on his feet

Trying to get him to eat his peas, well it ended up all
over me

All in all for my first day it's not been bad, right!!

Thanks for asking Neighbour

Well top of the afternoon to you neighbour

People today really have some funny sayings
Take what I just said. Top of the afternoon
Does the afternoon have a top if so it must also have
a bottom
Now let me think for a moment about this
and try to understand what I am saying
Aah so the top means you are in a good mood and
the afternoon is bright
And if I say to you bottom of the afternoon it
would imply
I am low, is that right? Am I right?

So hear what I did. I went to see my doctor with a
little tummy issue
He say have plenty of fruit.
You know an apple a day keep the doctor away
so I went to the store and stood there pondering
about what the doctor say
Now does he want me to buy an apple a day or fruits
not knowing what to do
A lovely lady passes my way, seeing the puzzled look
on my face

She asks are you OK.

I repeat what the doctor say. Then I say do I buy an apple a day or fruits

She too was baffled, and walk away – as I could not find fruits I buy an apple a day

But my problem did not go away. So I return to the doctor

He ask me if I buy the fruits. Then repeat an apple a day keep the doctor away

I say no I could not find anything called fruits, and so I buy an apple a day yet it did not keep you away I am still here today

This doctor look at me as if I was crazy then he say did you eat the apple

I say you did not say I had to eat the apple. So with a straight face he say Mr Jones what did you do with the apple? I said they are there in my tray turning a very funny colour. I cannot seem to get the little flies to keep away.

Then he wrote something on a paper and say take this to the shop

And hand it to the man or lady over the counter

Then take this other note when you get home please read it carefully

Be sure to do what the note says.

So off I went and did exactly what the note says.

Oh by the way

Did I tell you the time when I was told not to drink

And ended up in hospital they say I was D Hi drated

Then try to give me a drink

I told them but I was told by my doctor not to drink

After calling my doctor they put me in a room and lock the door

They try to say I was crazy but

I Mr Jones know perfectly well that their sentence

Is not logic

Now you have a pretty day neighbour

Dear neighbour

I woke up this morning, decided to go to church that's right church

There is a little one not too far from me, I am not a religious person but

I thought let's give it a go

So I took my hat down from the top of my wardrobe that was gathering dust.

Found a nice colour full dress to match. I look in the mirror yes, "looking good" I thought

And off I went. As I got closer to the church a tall man weirdly dressed

Staring at me with a smile full like the moon. As he stretched out his hand to greet me

I nervously gave a half moon smile. His grip was so tight I swear he broke my finger

Well he could have

As I entered the church the smell of incense overpowered me, I managed to take a seat near the back

Everyone passing by looked at me. Some smiling, some whispering.

I thought "what's with the whispering", I don't think this was a good idea to come. I wanted to leave but two women of size came and jammed themselves either side of me. What is this I thought there were more seats to go around. Then the tall figure of a man with white collar around his neck. That reminds me I must buy my cat a flea collar

This man had the biggest cross around his neck I have ever seen, ok I am exaggerating a bit

Anyway he starts to preach I don't know what he said I fell asleep – the song woke me up

Then I notice the collection plate coming round.

I scramble through my bag. I had no change. Only a $50 dollar note

I ask the person on my right have you got change showing my $50 dollar note, she whispers back " no."

I ask the woman on my left who was fanning herself like she can smell something

She gives me that side look you know that look when you don't want anyone to talk to you

Anyway there I was in-between these two women as the plate came closer.

In my face was this plate, I asked the person holding the plate if they have change, I got a blank stare. So I look in the collection plate plenty of change I put my hand in drop my note in the plate and start to take change I look up to find all eye on me, I said I am getting change

I felt my hand slipping away as their eyes were not impressed and leaving the change and my $50 dollar note on the plate

As the man on the platform with his full moon smile staring at me and says bless you my child.

as I watch my last $50 dollar getting further and further away, then a tap on my shoulder

By now I was vexed I turn round and snap do you want my shirt too I wasn't even wearing a shirt

A little voice said "you left the price tag on your hat" she said nervously

I was so embarrassed my hat was from a charity shop $2 dollar. I shrink down in my seat pretending I dropped something that's how I manage to crawl away.

Did I go back oh hell! no. I think I'll try bingo

Nice catching up with you neighbour

Hello nice person

Who is this, you can help me with a dollar or two I have
me drink bill to pay. Plus me false teeth want to fix, it
keep falling out me mouth. You did say hello neighbour
so where you live me can come live with you.

Me between homes at the moment I can come now how
far you at

You letter is nice so you must be a nice person

This place going to pull down tomorrow so best you
no write

But you can find me at the corner of First and
Second Street

It four bus stops away

But now don't forget to wire me the money John and
John off licence

Crossroads Second Street

See you nice person

Oh I forgot to tell you

You can buy me new shoes my old one keeps talking to
me it's old now it's been keeping me company for many
years everywhere I go it follows me

It got wet, one day I was sheltering from the rain

Must have fallen asleep, the bottom fell off when I tried to walk.

So now nice person can you send me some soon

Me thank you

Yes neighbour

Thank you for your kind letter as strangers we are it's so nice to be thought of

This Covid has got me good,

How I wake up each morning to face another day, I no longer turn on the news

Your letter was a real comfort to me. I thank you

Where there are good people there is hope I reach out to help others now.

Now, we all find comfort together. It's nice not to be alone during these times

You see I was not really a nice person before so I have been told. I never gave my neighbours any thought

I felt that I was somewhat better than them. I had everything that I wanted

Nice car, nice house, holiday 3 times a year they would say good morning to me but I always pretended I was on my phone. I came home one day from work coughing, sweating. The works

I could not get out of bed. That's when it dawned on me I had no one to help me

Not even my housekeeper, then the government called lockdown I was not prepared

Little did I know, the neighbours that I once ignored –
they came to my aid. I spend two weeks in hospital

Thanks to them and the hospital I made a good recovery,
others were not so fortunate

When I arrived home there were groceries on the kitchen
table. I saw your letter and that scripture you included

Philippians 2v4 it says – As you look out not only for
your own interests but also the interests of others

This gave me something to really think about

Now I have learnt what it is like to be a good neighbour

I have lost family members to this Covid

I am not alone in this loss of family but I have
gained friends

So thank you once again
Neighbour a distance away

Dear neighbour at a distant away

I received your letter a week ago sorry for the late reply

Things are not great at the moment. I have lost my job
the bills are piling up

I had to put Lion down, it was the hardest thing I've
ever done

We had that dog since he was a puppy. He was old and
in pain

The kids took it very hard

I have been searching the papers for a job I saw one for a
cleaner in a prestige

Apartment block. I am a qualified accountant but
nowhere was hiring so I was now desperate so when
I phoned up for the job I was told that they wanted
someone with more experience. How hard can it be
to clean

OK so I had a cleaner but raising 3 children and holding
down a fulltime job

It's not easy but I am not a proud woman that I won't do
what it takes to put food on the plate

My husband decided to pack up and return home to a warmer climate and before you ask it. I could not root up the kids just so, to a place that they did not know. And I had my job to think about at the time. We still have a mortgage on this house

For which he has not sent me a dime. Only a note saying I can keep the house if I give him a divorce. "kmt"

The time was not right. So we had a fight

Anyway things will sort themselves out

I have another interview tomorrow so I will let you know how I get on

Lollipop lady now I am sure to get this one how hard can it be

I wonder what flavour I'll be

Kind regards
Your neighbour

Dear neighbour

I went to visit Harry today. The weather has not been so great

And I am not that good on long walks the old bones are not all that strong any more

The rain does not help either.

But I keep out of the rain bad memory for me.

I visit the doctor last Thursday he said I have another 100 years ahead of me

He makes me chuckle

A nice young doctor, are you single? I can put in a word for you hahaha

I so enjoy your letters.

Tomorrow I have an appointment at the hospital

No not for me

I make buns for the staff and I'm knitting gloves for the little children

You are right life don't stay still for anyone

My Harry used to say why worry about what you cannot do. Do what you can do. I miss him.

Life doesn't get easy as one gets older, Harry's grave was looking the worse for wear

I get Mr Jones the caretaker to repair it for me he is very helpful

I know it's been 10 years now since my Harry left me he would have been the same age as Mr Jones. My Harry was one of a kind.

My Harry was very tall when he built our kitchen cupboards

He built it for his height and make me a stool to stand on, he has a funny sense of humour

He said that would stop me from eating all his biscuits hahaha

Oh we had some fun times then.

Oh yes dear I did promise next time I write I would tell you how I lost my Harry

One night we had such a bad storm we were on our way home.

It was a lovely day so we went for a picnic not our usual place

That why we took out bicycles but the weather changed

A great big storm came out of nowhere. Dark clouds, lots of thunder and lightning

It was only 3pm but you would have thought it was midnight that's how bad it was

The little bridge that we normally cross gave way, he was crossing first but I should have waited as he told me to.

He wanted to make sure it was safe but that night I did not I was behind him we both fell in the water that runs under the bridge it rained so heavy the little river was full in that short time

It was some hours before help came – when I came round

I was told my Harry was no more the water was very cold

He held me on his shoulder until help came so they said. That's my Harry a true gentleman

My hero.

I have to go now these buns won't bake themselves

It's been a long while now since I've had company for tea

But when you get the time please pass by

Thank you for your kindness

Your neighbour

Hi neighbour

I have plenty to tell you today I had to go stay with my nan and take her shopping

She is 70 but she would do whatever it takes to save a penny or two, I get so embarrassed sometimes.

I went shopping with her – she stopped at the greengrocers she wanted an apple so the man put it in the paper bag to weigh it, she told the man to weight the bag first

She then turned to me and said "my child you got to be smart, that bag will add an ounce to my apple that's extra money in his pocket" I say nothing on top of that the man did not give her back her penny change. She refused to leave the shop until she got her penny

Even though the man showed her in the till that he didn't have a penny

She still refused to leave the shop without her penny.

He had to go next door to get change so that she could have her penny but the queue was getting long behind me – I say "come on Nan it's just a penny"

Oops! my big mouth. She says "child you have got a lot to learn. Look at these people now how many pennies will he collect today, by the end of the day all that penny adds up.

Have you ever gone to a supermarket and you are short of one penny are they going to let you off that one penny? That's one penny to balance up their books."

After getting her penny she smiled at the man and said thank you like nothing ever happened and left the shop.

Then she went to the butcher she wanted some lamb chops

The butcher weighed out the chop the price was not to her liking so she told the man to cut off the extra fat on the lamb – the man say to her "there is not much to come off a little fat is good" Who told the man to say that by the time nan finish with the man she got the lamb chops for free fat and all and was banned from his shop. I was dying of embarrassment

Mr Bean has nothing on my nan but they must be family hahaha

Did I tell you when I brought my boyfriend for tea at hers

She asked him if he has all his teeth

Then she took hers out of her mouth to show him

I never saw him again.

She once helped out in a charity shop

A man came in wanted a pair of shoes one foot was displaying in the window

Any way he approached Nan and asked about the shoe, she said "of course you can try it on"

The man did not ask to try the shoe

Then he asked for the other foot. Yep she looked at him and looked at his feet

Well she said we only have the one so you get it for half price

He said he wanted both feet what for she asked looking down at his feet

Say no more, let's just say she did not stay there long.

Another time she used superglue for her dentures because she was too mean to buy the denture glue. Why waste money, this will do the same job she said

Or the time when she got a job as a lollipop woman

She spent the day lecturing the drivers on the road crossing

She backed up the traffic so much that they had to call the police

She got arrested for assaulting the officer

She claimed in court that she saw a wasp on the officer's head

Or the time I wanted a dog.

She got me a baby fox it's free she said

Next week we are going on holiday it's her first time flying
Pray for me

Kind regards
Your neighbour at a distance

Dear neighbour

I found your letter lying on the floor address unknown

So I opened it, your words were a comfort to my ears

I live nowhere sometimes a park bench is my bed or
under a tree

But as I read your letter I felt this was meant for me

I spent years wandering the street begging pocket change

Going to the bookies to keep warm when it's getting
too cold

Or find a pub that the people are nice sometimes they
would give me a bowl of soup

But you have told me life doesn't have to be this way

I don't drink, can't afford it anyway. There is a place I go
where they give away free food

I help them to carry the boxes they give me something at
the end of the day

One day one of them asked me what I do with the food if
I don't have nowhere to stay

I told him I gave some away.

I guess there are good people still about, this person gave
me a room

Thanks to your letter I have not let pride get in my way
and to accept help

I was throwing my old clothes away when I remembered
your letter

So here I am saying thank you

From a neighbour that was once from nowhere

A Note from the Author

When grandma used to cook she would share with her neighbours far and near, young and old

She had set a fine example of unselfish love

This has taught me to help my neighbours whether in words or deed

It also allows me to think about those far, far away